Scavenger Guides

CHICAGO

AN INTERACTIVE TRAVEL GUIDE FOR KIDS

Also available

Scavenger Guides Washington, DC

Scavenger Guides New York City

The Disney World Queue Line Scavenger Hunt

Scavenger Guides

CHICAGO

AN INTERACTIVE TRAVEL GUIDE FOR KIDS

Daniel Ireland

Three Leaf Press
Grand Haven, Michigan

Front cover photography: Navy Pier, Chicago © Noel Powell - Fotolia.com.

Back cover photography: Sue, Field Museum of Natural History © Daniel Ireland.

Photos courtesy of and copyright Free Range Stock, freerangestock.com: Lindsay Niles 17; Jaime Burciaga 20.

Photos courtesy of Morgue File, morguefile.com: Kenn W. Kiser 7, 8; D. Harder 18; Jenny Mehlenbeck 25.

Photos courtesy of Stock.xchng, sxc.hu: Charlotte Pickering 12; Marius Muresan 19; Nicole Shackelford 30; Raymond Wiggins 43; Fabiola de la Paz 44.

Photos published under Creative Commons Attribution 2.0 Generic license: Serge Melki 3; wanderingone 26; Brent Payne 28; nathanmac87 29; southie3 33; Marit & Toomas Hinnosaar 34; Charlotte Morrall 36; Steve Richmond 37; Lisamarie Babik 45; Brooke Novak 53. Photos published under Creative Commons Attribution-Share Alike 2.0 Generic license: pepsiline 27. Photos published under Creative Commons Attribution-No Derivative Works 2.0 Generic license: Jamie Fraser 32; John Gronberg 35; Bari D 38; Michael Lehet 52.

All other photos by author unless otherwise noted.

Published by Three Leaf Press
www.threeleafpress.com

Printed in the United States of America

First edition
ISBN: 978-0-9845866-0-8

CONTENTS

One way to get the most out of life is to look upon it as an adventure.

– William Feather

SCAVENGER ADVENTURE PLEDGE

I pledge to discover the natural, historical, and cultural beauty of the places I visit, to preserve them by respecting all local rules and customs, and to share my knowledge and experiences with others.

Amelia Neiman
_____
(print name here)

A NOTE TO PARENTS

Many parents have reservations about traveling with children, but travel doesn't have to end when you start a family. Travel is a wonderful time for children to learn and grow - no matter their age. It is also a wonderful time to grow as a family.

Traveling as a family is an incredible experience! Your child will grow in their knowledge and understanding of the world in which they live, and you'll see the world in a whole new way - through the uninhibited eyes of your child. Embrace traveling with your children, and you may find that your kids are capable of much more than you imagined!

This travel guide is for children visiting Chicago and their parents. It is designed to engage your child in their travels and enhance their observational skills. Presented as a scavenger hunt, this interactive travel challenge will also help parents capture those teachable moments while traveling. This guide contains many interesting facts and useful pieces of information to help your child learn about Chicago, but its most important role is as a tool to jump-start dialogue between you and your child.

This book is not a comprehensive travel guide to Chicago. Most children would rather experience the sights and sounds of a region first-hand than read about them in the pages of a travel book. There are numerous guides available on how to get to Chicago, where to stay, where to eat, and what to see and do, but they are written for adults. Use those guides to plan your trip. Cross-reference the places you plan to visit with the locations presented in this Scavenger Guide, and you will be well-prepared for a more in-depth travel experience with your child.

Each section of this guide presents several "clues" that challenge your child to find certain locations, identify items, or complete experiences throughout Chicago. Each completed item earns 10 points. At the end of their travels, children add up their points and collect their award certificate. For some children, the challenge of the hunt is motivation enough. As a parent, you may wish to attach an additional reward, such as money for a souvenir or the opportunity for the child to choose where the family dines their last night of vacation. You know your child best. Be creative. Above all, have fun and enjoy this truly unique travel experience with your child!

Family travel can be both fun and informative.

Have a wonderful trip!

WHERE IS CHICAGO?

Chicago is located on the southwestern shores of Lake Michigan in the state of Illinois. It is the third largest city in the United States and the largest city in the Midwestern U.S.

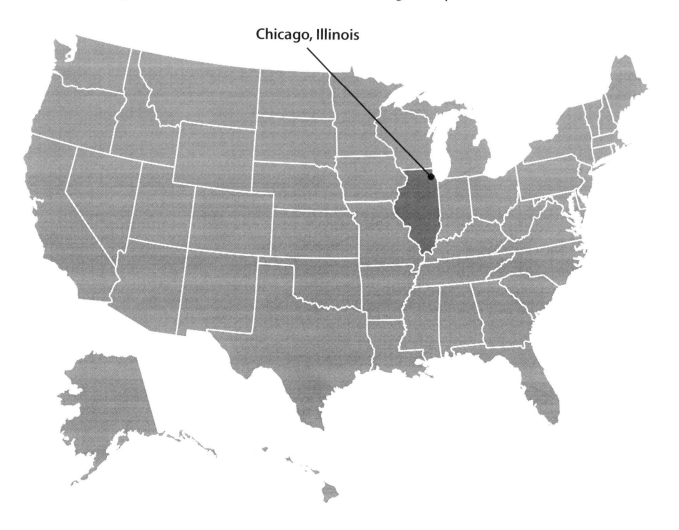

Chicago, Illinois

A SCAVENGER ADVENTURE

*A*re you ready for an adventure? Chicago is an amazing place! There is so much to see and do in the city. This scavenger hunt will help you get the most out of your experience. Can you complete each item and become a Scavenger Guides World Explorer?

Welcome to your Scavenger Hunt Adventure around Chicago! You'll need to use your eyes and your brain to solve these challenges. Your scavenger hunt will take you to many of the most popular and famous museums, landmarks, and other places of interest that make Chicago such an exciting place to visit. Whether you like sports, art, history, great food, or just experiencing new places, you'll find plenty to do in Chicago.

Have fun on your hunt and good luck. You will have an absolutely wonderful time exploring this great city!

How It Works

Your Scavenger Hunt Adventure has many challenges for you to complete during your visit to Chicago. You do not have to answer the challenges in order. Feel free to skip around as you visit various locations around the city. Also, don't feel you need to complete all the challenges in one day! Chicago is a big city, and it will take a lot of time and effort to complete your Scavenger Hunt Adventure. Correctly complete as many of the challenges on your scavenger hunt as you can. Keep track of each task you complete, then add up your points to win!

Before You Begin

Read all the questions in your Scavenger Hunt Adventure before you start. This will help you get familiar with all the different challenges you will be asked to complete at a specific location. This will help you use your time more efficiently and minimize repeated visits to the same site.

There are many ways to get around Chicago - by foot, bicycle, subway, taxi, bus, and even horse-drawn carriage!

▲ Horse-drawn carriages in downtown Chicago.

Helpful Hints

Here are some suggestions to help you in your search:

✔ Read each scavenger hunt question carefully before you begin.

✔ Questions have been grouped by topic. Mark the questions that go with the areas you plan to visit each day. Do this each morning as you plan your day.

✔ Look carefully all around you before you record your answers. Sometimes a second search will reveal things missed at first glance.

✔ Ask the staff at a museum or site's information desk. They can often point you in the right direction.

✔ Check out a site's map for clues.

✔ Question a guard or police officer.

✔ Read signs and plaques carefully. They often reveal clues that will lead you to

▲ Cooling off in Crown Fountain.

Chicago has over 550 parks, including 33 sand beaches and 10 bird and wildlife gardens.

the answer.

✔ Check to see if the site has a computer information system for visitors to use.

✔ Look in gift shops. The postcards and books there often cover the site's main points of interest.

✔ Don't be afraid to ask your parents and siblings for help! They might see something you have missed.

WHEN YOU FINISH

After you have completed as many challenges as you can, add up all the points from the challenges you solved. There is a handy worksheet at the end of the scavenger hunt to help you with this task. Compare your total score with the award chart at the bottom of the worksheet and collect your Scavenger Hunt Certificate. Can you reach the level of World Explorer? Have fun on your adventure!

WELCOME TO CHICAGO

*C*hicago is the largest city in the state of Illinois, and the third most populated city in the United States. It is located on the southwestern shores of Lake Michigan. There is a lot to see and do in Chicago. Here are our picks for the Top 10 Things for Kids in Chicago!

TOP 10 CHICAGO ATTRACTIONS

#10 Lincoln Park Zoo

This zoo, located on Chicago's north side, is one of the oldest zoos in the United States. The zoo houses over 1200 animals including the popular chimpanzees and gorillas in the Primate House. Best of all, admission to the zoo is free!

#9 Chicago Deep-Dish Pizza

Getting hungry from all that exploring? Dig into a Chicago-style deep-dish pizza. Chicago-style pizza has a buttery crust filled with toppings over 3 inches thick! Can you eat more than one piece?

#8 Museum of Science and Industry

Visit the largest science museum in the Western Hemisphere and explore a working coal mine, a German submarine captured during World War II, and a NASA Apollo 8 spacecraft. Many exhibits are interactive, including ToyMaker 3000 - a robotic assembly line where you can

▲ The German submarine U-505.

Although nicknamed the "Magnificent Mile," this famous section of North Michigan Avenue is only about three-quarters of a mile long.

order a toy top and watch as it is made.

#7 The Magnificent Mile

This shopping stretch along Michigan Avenue in downtown Chicago is popular with adults, but there are stores that kids will enjoy as well. Check out The Disney Store, American Girl, Apple Computers, The LEGO Store, and ESPN Zone.

#6 Millennium Park

Visit this large park in downtown Chicago at the north end of Grant Park. Have a picnic in the grass, catch a concert at

Pritzker Pavilion, stroll beautiful Lurie Garden, or cool off in Crown Fountain, an interactive water fountain where kids and adults get wet and wild!

#5 North Avenue Beach

Yes, there are beaches in downtown Chicago, and North Avenue Beach is one of the best! With beautiful blue water and sandy shores, you may feel like you're in the tropics rather than in one of the largest cities in the world.

#4 The "L"

The "L" is the name of Chicago's mass transit system. Unlike subway systems in other large cities, parts of the "L" are elevated above the streets giving riders an up-close look at many of Chicago's famous sites.

▲ Fun awaits at Chicago's Navy Pier.

The "L" is the second largest rapid transit system in the United States, after the New York City Subway.

#3 Navy Pier

Navy Pier is Chicago's top tourist attraction. It houses the Chicago Children's Museum, an IMAX theater, and numerous restaurants and shops. Navy Pier Park is a carnival on the pier where you can ride the Musical Carousel or take in the sights from the 150-foot-tall Ferris wheel.

#2 Museum Campus

Chicago's Museum Campus is located near the downtown lakeshore. You can watch a dolphin show at Shedd Aquarium, star gaze at Adler Planetarium, or stop by the Field Museum of Natural History to meet Sue, the largest, most complete T. rex in the world!

#1 Skyscrapers

When people think of Chicago, the first thing that comes to mind is often the city's tall buildings called skyscrapers.

▲ **View from the top of Willis Tower.**

Chicago is considered to be the birthplace of the skyscraper. The first skyscraper in the world was built in Chicago in 1885.

The first skyscraper in the world was built in Chicago in 1885. You can see many of the world's largest buildings in downtown Chicago, including Willis Tower (formerly Sears Tower) which stands as the tallest building in the United States. Visit the observation decks high atop Willis Tower or John Hancock Building for a bird's-eye-view of the city!

DISCOVER CHICAGO

Whatever you decide to do, Chicago is an exciting city to visit! Have fun, and don't forget to record your thoughts and observations in your daily journal at the back of this guide.

Ready to explore? Let's go on a Chicago Scavenger Hunt Adventure!

3 UNCOVER CLASSIC CHICAGO

*C*hicago is home to many things, including tall skyscrapers, a beautiful lakefront, and world-famous parks and museums. What comes to mind when you think of Chicago? For many people, they think of food. Chicago is renowned for its hot dogs and deep-dish pizza. Yum! Another Chicago icon is the "L," Chicago's elevated railroad. The "L" is a great way to get around downtown Chicago to see the sights!

CHICAGO HOT DOGS

Chicago is known for its great food. One of our favorites is the Chicago hot dog! Find out what makes a Chicago hot dog different.

❶ Find a hot dog vendor.

....10 points ⬜

❷ List 3 toppings found on a Chicago hot dog.

_____

_____

_____

.............................10 points ☐

3 Find out which topping is NEVER found on a Chicago hot dog.

_____

.............................10 points ☐

PIZZA PIZZA!

Now that's a big pizza! Chicago-style pizza

> **Chicago-style deep-dish pizza was invented at Pizzeria Uno, in Chicago, in 1943.**

▲ **The "L" traveling through the Loop.**

is a deep-dish pizza style developed in Chicago. It is so filling, it can be hard to eat more than one piece!

4 Find a pizza restaurant that serves Chicago-style deep-dish pizza.

.............................10 points ☐

5 Earn 10 extra points if you can eat a whole piece of deep-dish pizza.

.............................10 points ☐

6 Find Pizzeria Uno, the restaurant

GREAT CHICAGO FIRE

By the 1870s there were 300,000 people living in Chicago. At that time, most of the homes and buildings were built of wood. In the hot, dry summer of 1871, legend states that a cow in Mrs. O'Leary's barn kicked over a lantern and started the Great Chicago Fire.

No one knows for sure if this is how the fire really started, but the great fire of 1871 burned for 27 hours and destroyed 17,000 buildings. After the fire, buildings in Chicago had to be built of stones and bricks rather than wood.

Today you can visit several buildings that survived the fire, such as the Old Chicago Water Tower on upper Michigan Avenue and St. Michael's Church in Old Town. You can still see the black burn marks caused by the fire on the outside walls of St. Michael's.

▲ **Chicago Water Tower.**

where Chicago-style deep-dish pizza was invented in 1943.

....10 points ☐

The "L"

The Chicago subway system is nicknamed the "L." It is a shortened version of "elevated railroad" since parts of the system travel above the streets rather than underground like most city subway systems.

7 Find Chicago's mass transit system (subway) nicknamed the "L."

....10 points ☐

8 For a great view of the city, take a ride on the "L"! Earn 10 points if you ride the "L" in Chicago.

....10 points ☐

9 Find a subway map in a station .

....10 points ☐

10 Chicago "L" routes, called lines,

are identified by color. List 3 of the colors of "L" lines below. (hint: Look on a subway map.)

_____

_____

_____

....10 points ☐

Total Points For This Section

How did you do? Add up all your points from this section and write the number on the line below!

_____ **points**

NOTES

4 | PARKS & OUTDOORS SEARCH

When Chicago was founded in 1837, it choose the motto "Urbs in Horto" which in English means "City in a Garden." It's not hard to see why! Chicago has over 500 parks including sandy beaches, conservatories, lagoons, and gardens. In Chicago, you don't have to leave the big city to spend time in the great outdoors.

THE LAKESHORE

The Chicago Lakefront Trail is an 18-mile path in downtown Chicago along the coast of Lake Michigan. Walkers, joggers, bicyclists, and rollerbladers all enjoy the path which connects Chicago's many beaches and lakefront parks.

❶ Take a walk on Lakefront Trail, Chicago's 18-mile paved path along the Lake Michigan shoreline.

....10 points ☐

❷ Find a sandy beach in downtown Chicago and

have your picture taken on the shore.

.............................10 points ☐

❸ Find the large boat on North Avenue Beach that you can go inside. Walk up the stairs in the boat to the second floor for a great view of the city skyline!

.............................10 points ☐

▲ Along Chicago's Lakefront Trail.

CHICAGO RIVER

In 1900 engineers reversed the natural flow of water in the Chicago River to keep sewage and pollution from flowing into the city's fresh water supply. Look closely at the water in the Chicago River. What direction does the water flow?

❹ Walk across a bridge spanning the Chicago River.

.............................10 points ☐

❺ Take a walk on the Chicago Riverwalk which runs along the

Each year the Chicago River is dyed green for St. Patrick's Day. Forty gallons of vegetable dye are used to color the river for the celebration.

bank of the Chicago River.

....10 points ☐

6 The Chicago River has 38 movable bridges spanning it. Find one of the bridges over the river raised to allow boats to pass.

....10 points ☐

7 Find a plaque on a bridge honoring the first white men to pass through the Chicago River. In what year did they navigate the river?

Many boats travel up the Chicago River. Bridges open to allow tall boats to pass through.

....10 points ☐

GRANT PARK

Grant Park is a large public park located in the Loop district in downtown Chicago. It is often called Chicago's front yard. Many historic events have been held in Grant Park, including the visit of Pope John Paul II and President Barack Obama's Election

▲ Bridges open for boat traffic on the river.

Day victory speech. Residents and visitors celebrate some of Chicago's largest festivals in the park, such as Taste of Chicago and the Chicago Blues Festival.

8 There are many sculptures throughout Grant Park. Find a Native American on horseback.

....10 points ☐

9 Find Buckingham Fountain, one of the largest fountains in the world. The fountain shoots water 150 feet into the air! Toss a coin in the fountain and make a wish.

....10 points ☐

10 Find a field shaped like a diamond. Name an activity you think is played on this field.

_____

....10 points ☐

11 Find a statue of the 16th president of the United States. (hint: You can also find him on the U.S. penny.)

....10 points ☐

▲ Buckingham Fountain in Grant Park.

Grant Park is often referred to as Chicago's front yard. Many statues and modern sculptures can be found throughout the park.

MILLENNIUM PARK

Millennium Park sits in the northwestern corner of Grant Park. You can play in a fountain, go ice skating, stroll through a garden, and attend a music concert all within the park.

12 Find a large silver jelly bean. Lay on your back under the bean and find your reflection on its surface.

....10 points ☐

▲ *Cloud Gate* reflecting the city skyline.

The glass blocks of Crown Fountain are actually high-tech LED video screens which project the faces of individual Chicagoans.

13 Find a bandshell that looks like the unfurling sails of a massive ship.

....10 points ☐

14 Find a fountain with human faces projected on glass block towers. How many glass block video towers stand in Crown Fountain?

_____

....10 points ☐

15 Find a bridge that curves like a snake.

....10 points ☐

16 Find a wooden footbridge over water in a garden.

....10 points ☐

17 Find Millennium Monument, a semi-circle of 40-foot Greek Doric columns located in Wrigley Square in the northwest section of the park. The names of Millennium Park's founders are etched in stone at the base of the monument.

....10 points ☐

TOTAL POINTS FOR THIS SECTION

How did you do? Add up all your points from this section and write the number on the line below!

_____ **points**

NOTES

5 BUILDINGS & LANDMARKS

*C*hicago is the birthplace of the skyscraper. In 1885, the first steel skyscraper in the world was erected in Chicago. Today, Chicago is home to some of the tallest buildings in the world. In addition to its skyscrapers, Chicago has many historic sites and landmarks. The city is also well known for its public sculptures and monuments. Most of these works of art can be found outdoors.

MAGNIFICENT MILE

Home to many large department stores, the Magnificent Mile is located along Michigan Avenue north of the Chicago River. It is the most popular place in Chicago to shop.

❶ Find a street performer on Michigan Avenue. Have your picture taken with the performer.

....10 points ☐

❷ Find a building with an apple on it.

....10 points ☐

❸ Find a sculpture of a moose.

....10 points ☐

❹ Find a person on the street pretending to be a statue.

....10 points ☐

JOHN HANCOCK CENTER

❺ Find the John Hancock Center, a black building with large Xs on the exterior. These Xs form a skeleton that help the building stand upright during heavy winds.

....10 points ☐

❻ Take an elevator up to the observatory at the top of the John Hancock Center. Make sure you hang on tight! These elevators rocket up at 1,800 feet per minute,

▲ John Hancock Center soars above the Old Water Tower.

The John Hancock Center's 44th-floor sky lobby features America's highest indoor swimming pool.

making them the fastest elevators in North America!

....10 points ☐

7 Find a waterfall outside the John Hancock Center.

....10 points ☐

CHICAGO WATER TOWER

The limestone Chicago Water Tower, which resembles a castle, was one of the few buildings to survive the Great Chicago Fire of 1871.

8 Find a plaque on the Old Water Tower designating it the first American Water Landmark.

....10 points ☐

9 Who was the mayor of Chicago when the tower was designated an American Water Landmark?

_____

▲ **The entrance to the ornate Tribune Tower.**

The Chicago Water Tower is the second-oldest water tower in the United States, after the Louisville Water Tower in Louisville, Kentucky.

....10 points ▢

10 What does the city of Chicago use the Old Water Tower for today? (hint: Go inside.)

_____

....10 points ▢

TRIBUNE TOWER

Tribune Tower is the home of the Chicago Tribune newspaper. The neo-Gothic design was the winning entry from a competition in 1922 to design "the most beautiful and eye-catching building in the world."

Watch radio DJs at work through the ground-level studio windows of WGN Radio which broadcasts from the Tribune Tower.

▲ **Artifact on the Tribune Tower's wall.**

11 Find the statue of Nathan Hale before the entrance doors to the Tribune Tower. Nathan Hale was a soldier for the Continental Army during the American Revolutionary War.

....10 points ▢

12 Find rock fragments and other artifacts from famous sites around the world embedded in the exterior walls of the Tribune

THE BILLY GOAT CURSE

Chicagoans are some of the most loyal sports fans anywhere. Perhaps no fans are more faithful than fans of the Chicago Cubs baseball team. The Cubs have not won a championship in over 100 years, which is longer than any other professional sports team. Some people say it is because of the Billy Goat Curse.

▲ **The famous Billy Goat Tavern on Michigan Avenue.**

The Billy Goat Curse was placed on the team in 1945 when Billy Sianis, owner of the Billy Goat Tavern, was asked to leave a World Series game at Wrigley Field. It seems the smell of his pet goat, which he had brought along to the game, was bothering other fans. Mr. Sianis grew angry and declared, "Them Cubs, they ain't gonna win no more."

The Cubs lost the game, lost the Series, and have not been back to the World Series since.

Tower. There are more than 100 artifacts embedded in the walls of the Tribune Tower. List your four favorite artifacts below.

_____

_____

_____

_____

...................................10 points ☐

⓭ Find a cat in the Aesop's Fables Screen over the entrance doors

to the Tribune Tower.

....10 points ☐

WRIGLEY BUILDING

The Wrigley Building is a skyscraper built by chewing gum tycoon William Wrigley Jr. to headquarter his gum company. It was Chicago's first air-conditioned office building.

▲ Don't know the time? Check one of the many dials on the Wrigley Building's clock tower.

Recently a piece of steel recovered from the World Trade Center in New York City was added to the Tribune Tower's collection of historical artifacts.

14 Find the gleaming white Wrigley Building, headquarters of the Wrigley Company, at the south end of the Magnificent Mile.

....10 points ⬡

15 How many clock dials are featured on the Wrigley Building clock tower?

_____

....10 points ⬡

16 Whose statue can be found on Plaza of the Americas between the

At night, the Wrigley Building's white terra-cotta exterior is brightly lit with floodlights.

▲ **Navy Pier's giant Ferris wheel.**

Wrigley Building and Realtor Building?

_____

....10 points ⬡

NAVY PIER

Navy Pier is a large pier on Lake Michigan close to downtown Chicago. It's the place

where residents and tourists come together to enjoy a day of fun on Lake Michigan. Take a ride on the 150-foot-tall Ferris wheel, then watch a show at the IMAX theater. You can also see a performance by the Chicago Shakespeare Theater or visit the Chicago Children's Museum. Crystal Gardens is an indoor tropical garden complete with palm trees and flowering plants. Don't miss the dancing "leapfrog" fountains!

▲ Having fun on the Musical Carousel.

17 Find the Ferris wheel on Navy Pier. What color are the cars on the Ferris wheel?

_____

....10 points ☐

18 Find a place where some animals might be getting dizzy. List the name of your favorite animal on the ride.

_____

....10 points ☐

Navy Pier was once used as a Navy training facility during World War II. U.S. sailors and pilots, including future President George H. W. Bush, trained at Navy Pier.

⓳ Find a sculpture of kids playing. Count the statues. How many children are playing together?

_____

....10 points ☐

Chicago Theatre

The Chicago Theatre is an historic theater located in the Loop area of downtown Chicago. The theater was built in 1921 to show movies. Today you can see plays,

▲ **The historic Chicago Theatre.**

magic shows, comedy acts, and music concerts at the theater.

⓴ The Chicago Theatre is a famous symbol of Chicago. It appears in many movies, TV shows, photographs, and works of art. Join in this tradition and take a picture of a family member in front of the famous theater.

....10 points ☐

㉑ Find the Y-shaped figure behind the horizontal word Chicago on the side of the marquee. This is a city symbol representing the Chicago River.

....10 points ☐

22 Find the plaque under the Chicago Theatre marquee that was dedicated in honor of Roger Ebert. On July 12, 2005, Mayor Richard Daley declared a special day for Mr. Ebert, a famous Chicago film critic.

....10 points ☐

CHICAGO PICASSO

The Chicago Picasso is a sculpture by Pablo Picasso in Daley Plaza in the Chicago Loop. The sculpture is 50 feet tall and weighs 162 tons! Musical performances, farmer's markets, and other events are held around the Picasso statue, making it a well-known meeting spot for Chicago residents.

23 Find the famous Chicago Picasso sculpture in Daley Plaza outside the

▲ Picasso's unnamed sculpture stands in Daley Plaza.

Visitors to Daley Plaza can often be seen sliding down the steel base of the Chicago Picasso sculpture.

Richard J. Daley Center.

....10 points ☐

24 Picasso never explained what the sculpture was intended to represent. Look at the sculpture Picasso created. What do you think it is a sculpture of?

_____

....10 points ☐

25 Find the eternal flame memorial in Daley Plaza. Who does it honor?

_____

_____

....10 points ☐

CHICAGO CULTURAL CENTER

The Chicago Cultural Center is an arts and culture center featuring free art exhibits, music, dance, and theater events. Be sure

▲ A fountain splashes in Daley Plaza.

Many movie scenes have been filmed in and around Daley Plaza, including the *Blues Brothers*, *The Fugitive*, and *The Dark Knight*.

to check out the center's two magnificent stained-glass domes!

26 Enter the Chicago Cultural Center at the Washington Street entrance and find the grand staircase. Take a peek at the top of the staircase and find the 38-foot Tiffany glass dome, the largest Tiffany dome in the world.

....10 points ☐

27 What was the Chicago Cultural Center building before it was converted to an arts and culture

> **The Chicago Cultural Center serves as the city's official reception site where the mayor welcomes presidents, royalty, and other leaders.**

▲ **Inside the Chicago Cultural Center.**

center? (hint: You can ask at the center's information desk.)

_____

....10 points ☐

28 Visit an art exhibit inside the Chicago Cultural Center.

....10 points ☐

WILLIS TOWER

Willis Tower, formerly named Sears Tower, is a 108-story skyscraper in Chicago. At the time of its completion in 1973 it was the tallest building in the world. Today, Willis Tower is the tallest building in the United States and the fifth-tallest building in the world.

29 Find Willis Tower. If you take the 60-second ride on the elevators to the observation Skydeck, you may feel the building sway on a windy day!

..............................10 points ☐

30 Find a "glass balcony" in the Skydeck on the 103rd floor of

On the Skydeck you can experience how Willis Tower sways on a windy day. On a clear day you can see Indiana, Michigan, and Wisconsin.

▲ **Enjoy a panoramic view of the city from the Willis Tower Skydeck.**

Willis Tower. If you dare, stand in the glass box and look through the floor to the street 1,353 feet below!

..............................10 points ☐

31 Find the transmission antennas on top of Willis Tower. Many radio and TV stations transmit off the top of the tower.

....10 points ☐

SOLDIER FIELD

Soldier Field is a football stadium located on the Lake Michigan shoreline in Chicago. It is home to the NFL's Chicago Bears.

32 Find a bronze mural of soldiers and their families outside Soldier Field. Soldier Field, home of the Chicago Bears football team, is dedicated as a memorial to American soldiers who died in wars.

..............................10 points ☐

Soldier Field can seat 61,500 fans for a Chicago Bears football game, making it the smallest stadium in the National Football League.

33 Which U.S. president is quoted on the back of the monument?

_____

....10 points ☐

34 Soldier Field was renovated in 2003, but it still retains the Greek-style columns from its original structure. Find the old Greek Doric columns below the new, modern stadium

▲ Soldier Field honors American soldiers.

bowl. Some fans refer to the new stadium as the "Spaceship on Soldier Field."

....10 points ☐

WRIGLEY FIELD

Built in 1914, Wrigley Field is the second-oldest ballpark in Major League Baseball behind Boston's Fenway Park (1912). It is the home ballpark of the Chicago Cubs. Wrigley Field is nicknamed "The Friendly Confines." The area surrounding the ballpark is typically referred to as Wrigleyville.

㉟ Find the statue of Harry Caray, former announcer for the Chicago Cubs professional baseball team, standing outside Wrigley Field near the Addison-Sheffield street corner.

....10 points ☐

㊱ Find the famous red sign over the main entrance to Wrigley Field which reads, "Wrigley Field, Home

▲ Behind home plate at Wrigley Field.

From 1921-1970 Wrigley Field was also home of the Chicago Bears of the National Football League. It is the second oldest major league ballpark after Boston's Fenway Park.

of Chicago Cubs."

....10 points ☐

37 Wrigley Field is one of the last
parks to maintain a hand-turned
scoreboard. Find the big green
scoreboard mounted above the
center field bleachers.

....10 points ☐

TOTAL POINTS FOR THIS SECTION

*How did you do? Add up all your points
from this section and write the number on
the line below!*

_____ **points**

NOTES

6 DISCOVER CHICAGO'S MUSEUMS

*I*f you like museums, Chicago is the place for you! Chicago has some of the best museums in the world. You can explore hands-on science and technology at the Museum of Science and Industry. Go stargazing at Adler Planetarium and imagine what it would be like to be a real astronaut. Spend an afternoon digging for dinosaur bones at the Field Museum. There is so much to see and do, it may be hard to decide where to begin!

ADLER PLANETARIUM

The Adler Planetarium was the first planetarium built in the Western Hemisphere. It was founded in 1930.

❶ Find *Man Enters the Cosmos*, a bronze sculpture of a sundial located outside the Adler Planetarium. What year was the statue erected?

....10 points ☐

2 Find the Gemini 12 spacecraft, a capsule flown into space by Astronauts Jim Lovell and Buzz Aldrin in 1966.

..........................10 points ☐

3 Find the lunar gravity simulator. Lie on the slider board and try a lunar leap to feel what it's like to jump on the Moon!

..........................10 points ☐

▲ Atwood Sphere in Adler Planetarium.

ART INSTITUTE OF CHICAGO

The Art Institute of Chicago is one of America's premier fine art museums. It is most famous for its collections of Impressionist, Post-Impressionist, and American paintings. You can view famous works of art from artists such as Claude Monet, Pierre-Auguste Renoir, Paul Cezanne, Georges Seurat, and Grant Wood.

4 Find the painting *Sunday Afternoon*

Adler Planetarium is part of Chicago's Museum Campus along with the Shedd Aquarium and the Field Museum of Natural History.

on the Island of La Grande Jatte by Georges Seurat. This famous work is an example of pointillism - a style of painting with small dots of primary colors (red, green, and blue). Look closely at Seurat's painting for the many tiny dots of paint. Then back up and watch as your eyes mix these color dots into a fuller range of colors!

....10 points ☐

5 Find a painting by Claude Monet. What is the name of the painting?

The Chicago Art Institute's entrance on Michigan Avenue is guarded by two bronze lion statues.

▲ **Lions outside the Chicago Art Institute.**

_____

....10 points ☐

6 Find the painting *American Gothic* by the artist Grant Wood. What is the man in the painting holding in his hand?

_____

....10 points ☐

FIELD MUSEUM OF NATURAL HISTORY

The Field Museum of Natural History, located on Museum Campus, is one of the top cultural attractions in Chicago. On May 17, 2000, the Field Museum unveiled Sue, the most complete and best-preserved Tyrannosaurus rex fossil yet discovered.

7 Find Sue, the Tyrannosaurus rex fossil. How old is Sue?

_____

....10 points ☐

▲ **Sue the Tyrannosaurus rex.**

8 Find the elephants, large land mammals native to Africa, standing in the Stanley Field Hall.

....10 points ☐

Sue is the largest and most complete Tyrannosaurus currently known. She is 42 feet long and stands 13 feet high at the hips.

9 Find the McDonald's Fossil Prep Lab. Look through the windows of the lab and watch as paleontologists prepare real fossil bones for scientific study.

....10 points ☐

MUSEUM OF SCIENCE AND INDUSTRY

The Museum of Science and Industry is housed in the former Palace of Fine Arts from the 1893 World's Fair. Tour the U-505, one of just two German submarines captured during World War II. Board the stainless steel Pioneer Zephyr passenger train from the 1930s. In the ToyMaker 3000 exhibit you can see up close how a toy is manufactured. Watch as 12 moving robots gather the toy parts, *assemble them, and then package your toy for you to take home! Be sure to check out the detailed miniature model of Chicago, complete with working trains and subway!*

❿ Find a cobblestone street in Chicago from the early 1900s. Explore the street and have your picture taken in front of an old storefront.

....10 points ☐

The museum's Science Storms exhibit features a 40-foot water vapor tornado and a tsunami tank!

▲ **The Pioneer Zephyr passenger train.**

11 Find the three-wheeled Spirit of America - the car that broke two world land speed records before being donated to the museum in 1965. What was the fastest speed the Spirit of America reached?

_____

....10 points ☐

12 Find a World War II German U-505 submarine. What was the name of the U.S. Navy captain who captured the submarine?

_____

....10 points ☐

13 Find the ToyMaker 3000 assembly line exhibit. Follow the assembly line and watch a toy being made by robots!

....10 points ☐

TOTAL POINTS FOR THIS SECTION

How did you do? Add up all your points from this section and write the number on the line below!

_____ **points**

NOTES

7 | CHICAGO ANIMAL SAFARI

*A*n animal safari in Chicago? You bet! Chicago is a great place to see animals! Take in a dolphin show at Shedd Aquarium's Oceanarium, one of the city's most popular attractions. Then get a diver's-eye view of sharks in Wild Reef. Lincoln Park Zoo is one of the oldest zoos in the United States. Stare into the eyes of a lowland gorilla, try your hand at milking a dairy cow, then ride the Endangered Species Carousel. Lincoln Park Zoo is open 365 days a year and admission is free! Brookfield Zoo, in the Chicago suburb of Brookfield, is one of the largest zoos in the United States. It was the first zoo in America to exhibit giant pandas!

SHEDD AQUARIUM

The John G. Shedd aquarium contains over 2,100 species including fish, marine mammals, birds, snakes, amphibians, and insects. Shedd Aquarium also features an Oceanarium with marine mammals, such as sea otters,

Pacific white-sided dolphins, and belugas.

1 The basic design of Shedd Aquarium is taken from classical Greek architecture with Doric columns, a formal staircase, and a dome. Find the Doric columns at the entrance of Shedd Aquarium. How many Doric columns stand at the entrance?

_____

....10 points ⬭

▲ **Shedd Aquarium on Museum Campus.**

2 Find a man holding a fish outside the aquarium. (hint: He is near the side entrance.)

....10 points ⬭

3 Find the see-through floor and "walk on water." Name one sea creature you see gliding beneath your feet.

_____

....10 points ⬭

In 1930, railroad tank cars transported one million gallons of seawater from Florida to Chicago for Shedd Aquarium's saltwater exhibits.

4 Find a shell on the ceiling.

....10 points ☐

LINCOLN PARK ZOO

Lincoln Park Zoo is often described as "a world of wildlife in the shadow of skyscrapers." It is one of the oldest zoos in the United States. The zoo was founded in 1868.

5 Find a statue of a bear with a fish in its mouth.

▲ Playful bears welcome you to the zoo.

Originally opened in 1927, primates of all shapes and sizes can be seen swinging through the trees inside the historic Helen Brach Primate House.

....10 points ☐

6 Find the old burr oak tree which has stood at the park location since 1830, three years before the city of Chicago was founded. Now that's an old tree!

....10 points ☐

7 Find the Helen Brach Primate House. Photograph members of your family posing as monkeys inside the Primate House.

....10 points ☐

8 Find a statue of wolves.

....10 points ☐

9 Find the Farm-in-the-Zoo and watch a cow being milked.

....10 points ☐

BROOKFIELD ZOO

Brookfield Zoo is also known as the Chicago Zoological Park. It is located in the Chicago suburb of Brookfield, Illinois. This large 216-acre zoo houses 450 species of animals, a children's zoo, and butterfly garden.

10 Visit the lowland gorillas in Tropic World. Built in the 1980s, Tropic World was the first fully-indoor rain forest simulation in the world.

....10 points ☐

11 Find Roosevelt Fountain, erected in memory of Theodore Roosevelt,

▲ A lowland gorilla in Brookfield Zoo's indoor rain forest.

Brookfield Zoo was one of the first zoos to use moats and ditches, instead of cages, to separate animals from visitors.

twenty-sixth president of the United States. In what year was the fountain dedicated?

....10 points ☐

⓬ Find the large bronze statue of Olga the Atlantic walrus in the sea mammal exhibit. Olga entertained visitors to the zoo between 1962 and 1988.

▲ Posing with Olga the Atlantic walrus.

....10 points ☐

⓭ Watch a dolphin show at the Seven Seas Dolphin Arena. Brookfield Zoo has been caring for dolphins for over 50 years!

....10 points ☐

⓮ Visit one of Brookfield Zoo's newest exhibits, Great Bear Wilderness. List one or more actions you can take to help save the bears.

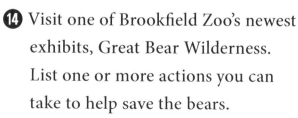

Great Bear Wilderness features North American animals including polar bears, brown bears, bison, bald eagles, and Mexican gray wolves.

_____

_____

_____

_____

....10 points ☐

15 What animal is the symbol of the
Chicago Zoological Society? (hint:
Look on signs throughout the zoo.)

_____

....10 points ☐

TOTAL POINTS FOR THIS SECTION

How did you do? Add up all your points
from this section and write the number on
the line below!

_____ **points**

NOTES

PARENT CLUES

Parents, here is your chance to contribute to the hunt! Use the spaces below to add additional clues for your child to solve in and around Chicago. Try including places to find, foods to try, or experiences to enjoy. Have fun!

_____

_____

10 points ☐

_____

_____

10 points ☐

_____

_____

10 points ☐

_____

_____

10 points ☐

_____

10 points ☐

10 points ☐

10 points ☐

10 points ☐

10 points ☐

10 points ☐

60

10 points ☐

10 points ☐

10 points ☐

10 points ☐

10 points ☐

10 points ☐

10 points ☐

10 points ☐

10 points ☐

10 points ☐

NOTES

HOW DID YOU DO?

It's time to be rewarded for all your hard work! Use the area below to add up your total points from each section. Then add up your grand total and claim your award! Fill out your name and today's date on the award certificate. Then have your mom or dad sign it. Great job!!

UNCOVER CLASSIC CHICAGO   _____ **POINTS**

PARKS & OUTDOORS SEARCH   _____ **POINTS**

BUILDINGS & LANDMARKS   _____ **POINTS**

DISCOVER CHICAGO'S MUSEUMS   _____ **POINTS**

CHICAGO ANIMAL SAFARI   _____ **POINTS**

PARENT CLUES   _____ **POINTS**

_____ **TOTAL POINTS**

300-499 POINTS .... **TRAVEL GUIDE**
500-699 POINTS .... **TRAVEL ADVENTURER**
700+ POINTS .... **WORLD EXPLORER**

CERTIFICATE OF TRAVEL EXCELLENCE

This award certifies that

_____

has successfully achieved the level of

TRAVEL GUIDE

in Scavenger Guides Chicago Scavenger Adventure

_____   _____
DATE   PARENT

TRAVEL GUIDE
300-499 POINTS

CERTIFICATE OF TRAVEL EXCELLENCE

This award certifies that

_____

has successfully achieved the level of

TRAVEL ADVENTURER

in Scavenger Guides Chicago Scavenger Adventure

_____   _____
DATE   PARENT

TRAVEL ADVENTURER
500-699 POINTS

CERTIFICATE OF TRAVEL EXCELLENCE

This award certifies that

_____

has successfully achieved the level of

WORLD EXPLORER

in Scavenger Guides Chicago Scavenger Adventure

_____   _____
DATE   PARENT

WORLD EXPLORER
700+ POINTS

KEEPING A TRAVEL JOURNAL

Keeping a journal of your travel adventures is a wonderful way to preserve memories. It makes a great souvenir of your trip to Chicago! The following section of this guide provides you with space to record your daily writings.

Make a habit to write in your travel journal each night before bed. As you record your thoughts, reflect back on your day. Use your five senses to describe your adventures! What did you see? What smells filled your nose? Are there sounds that caught your attention? What tastes did you experience? What touches and textures do you remember?

If possible, take pictures each day during your travels. Photographs from your trip will complement your journal. If you do not have a camera of your own, ask your parents if you can be involved taking pictures with them.

When you return home, be sure to check out the digital storytelling page on the Scavenger Guides website. You will learn how to combine recordings of your daily journal writings with digital pictures from your trip to create a multimedia travel video starring you! Visit http://www.scavengerguides.com to learn how!

The following page shows a sample journal entry. This is only an example. Feel free to record anything you wish from your travel experiences. Have fun with your journal!

MY TRAVEL JOURNAL   DAY 1

DATE _June 16_

SIGHTS _tall buildings, lots of cars, street performers_

SMELLS _flowers in the park, pizza!!_

SOUNDS _cars honking, performers drumming, people talking_

TASTES _salty peanuts, sour candy_

TOUCHES _cold seats on the trolley, soft grass_

DAILY LOG

Today we walked downtown and watched the street performers on Michigan Avenue. I saw a man juggling five bowling balls! I took my picture with him. We also watched two boys play their drums. Then we rode the trolley to Navy Pier. My brother and I played in a fountain. We got really wet, but it was a lot of fun! After we dried off, dad took us on the Ferris wheel!

MY TRAVEL JOURNAL   DAY 1

DATE _____

SIGHTS_____

SMELLS_____

SOUNDS_____

TASTES_____

TOUCHES_____

DAILY LOG

_____

_____

_____

_____

_____

_____

My Travel Journal   Day 2

Date _____

Sights _____

Smells _____

Sounds _____

Tastes _____

Touches _____

Daily Log

_____

_____

_____

_____

_____

_____

MY TRAVEL JOURNAL   DAY 3

DATE _____

SIGHTS_____

SMELLS_____

SOUNDS_____

TASTES_____

TOUCHES_____

DAILY LOG

_____

_____

_____

_____

_____

_____

MY TRAVEL JOURNAL   DAY 4

DATE _____

SIGHTS_____

SMELLS_____

SOUNDS_____

TASTES_____

TOUCHES_____

DAILY LOG

_____

_____

_____

_____

_____

_____

MY TRAVEL JOURNAL

DAY 5

DATE _____

SIGHTS_____

SMELLS_____

SOUNDS_____

TASTES_____

TOUCHES_____

DAILY LOG

_____

_____

_____

_____

_____

_____

MY TRAVEL JOURNAL   DAY 6

DATE _____

SIGHTS_____

SMELLS_____

SOUNDS_____

TASTES_____

TOUCHES_____

DAILY LOG

_____

_____

_____

_____

_____

_____

My Travel Journal   Day 7

Date _____

Sights_____

Smells_____

Sounds_____

Tastes_____

Touches_____

Daily Log

_____

_____

_____

_____

_____

MY TRAVEL JOURNAL   DAY 8

DATE _____

SIGHTS_____

SMELLS_____

SOUNDS_____

TASTES_____

TOUCHES_____

DAILY LOG

_____

_____

_____

_____

_____

_____

MY TRAVEL JOURNAL

DAY 9

DATE _____

SIGHTS_____

SMELLS_____

SOUNDS_____

TASTES_____

TOUCHES_____

DAILY LOG

_____

_____

_____

_____

_____

MY TRAVEL JOURNAL

DAY 10

DATE _____

SIGHTS_____

SMELLS_____

SOUNDS_____

TASTES_____

TOUCHES_____

DAILY LOG

_____

_____

_____

_____

_____

_____

My Travel Journal   Day 11

Date _____

Sights_____

Smells_____

Sounds_____

Tastes_____

Touches_____

Daily Log

_____

_____

_____

_____

_____

MY TRAVEL JOURNAL

DATE _____

SIGHTS_____

SMELLS_____

SOUNDS_____

TASTES_____

TOUCHES_____

DAILY LOG

_____

_____

_____

_____

_____

MY TRAVEL JOURNAL   DAY 13

DATE _____

SIGHTS_____

SMELLS_____

SOUNDS_____

TASTES_____

TOUCHES_____

DAILY LOG

_____

_____

_____

_____

_____

_____

MY TRAVEL JOURNAL

DATE _____

SIGHTS_____

SMELLS_____

SOUNDS_____

TASTES_____

TOUCHES_____

DAILY LOG

_____

_____

_____

_____

_____

_____

MY TOP 10

Earlier we gave you our picks for the Top 10 Things for Kids in Chicago. Now it's your turn! Think about all the things you did in Chicago. What were your favorites? Use the space below to record your picks for the best things to do in Chicago. Complete this page the last day of your visit. You can share this list with your friends when they plan their own Chicago adventure!

#10 _____

_____

#9 _____

_____

#8 _____

_____

#7 _____

_____

#6 _____

_____

#5 _____

_____

#4 _____

_____

#3 _____

_____

#2 _____

_____

#1 _____

_____

TIPS FOR TAKING GREAT VACATION PHOTOS

In addition to keeping a daily journal, you may also wish to take pictures during your travels. While your journal is a written record of your travel experiences, images are snapshots in time - visual memories to enjoy and share with others long after your vacation is over. Photographs from your trip will complement your journal and help you relive those great vacation memories!

This chapter will give you tips on how to take great vacation photos. Practice these techniques and soon you'll be taking shots like the pros. Above all, experiment and have fun with your photography!

FUN CREATIVE PROJECTS

After you return from your vacation you'll want to share your photos with family and friends. Pictures make wonderful souvenirs, and they are a great way to share your vacation experiences with others. There are also many things that you can do with your photos. Here are some fun activities you might consider.

✔ Create a framed collage of your favorite vacation photos to hang in your room.

✔ Design a vacation scrapbook.

✔ Create an online gallery to display your trip photos.

✔ Make your own vacation souvenir. Many online photo stores allow you to upload your digital pictures and place them on shirts, mugs, mouse pads, and other items.

✔ Combine your digital pictures and journal writings with motion effects and music to create a multimedia travel video to share with family and friends. Visit http://www. scavengerguides.com to learn how!

Don't Have A Camera?

If you do not have a camera of your own, ask your parents if you can be involved taking pictures with them. Have your parents show you how to operate the camera. Ask if you can take some practice photos at home with their assistance. Another option is to use a disposable or single-use camera. These cameras come pre-loaded with a fixed number of photos (usually 24 or 36). When all of the pictures are taken, the entire camera is returned for processing. Single-use cameras are widely available for less than $10.

A Message For Parents

If possible, give your child their own camera to use. If that's not feasible, let them share the picture taking responsibilities with you. Spend some time before your trip showing them how to operate your camera correctly and responsibly. Have your child read the tips in this chapter, but don't over-supervise. Allow them the freedom to compose and take their own photos. You may be surprised at the pictures they take. Not only will you have a visual history of your trip from your child's perspective, but you may also find yourself in a few more vacation photos! While they certainly will enjoy the pictures you take, the experience and memories will mean more if they are fully involved in the process.

Tip #1: Know How To Use Your Camera & Settings

It's important that you know how to operate your camera before you go on your vacation. A lot of problems can be avoided if you know how your camera and all its settings work before you leave home. Here is a checklist of things to review.

▲ **Take time before your trip to learn all the settings and features on your camera.**

✔ Read the instructions that came with your camera, or ask your mom and dad to show you how their camera works. Know what settings to use for various shots.

✔ If your camera has a telephoto lens, find out how to zoom in and out.

✔ Learn how your flash works.

✔ Find out if there are any special features such as autofocus or red-eye reduction that can help you take better pictures.

✔ Practice using your camera by taking some pictures at home before your trip. This will help you get comfortable with your camera and learn what you can do with it.

✔ Practice keeping the camera still while taking pictures to prevent blurry photos. Breathe in while holding your camera close to your face and press the shutter button gently, so the camera doesn't shake.

TIP #2: CARRY YOUR CAMERA WITH YOU ALL THE TIME

Make it a habit to always carry your camera with you wherever you go. You never know when an opportunity for a great shot will occur. Be ready! You don't want to miss that once-in-a-lifetime moment.

▲ Use the zoom feature on your camera to get in close for amazing shots!

✔ Take your camera along wherever you go.

✔ Carry your camera in a case with a clip or belt loops to attach to your waist. You can also use a waist or "fanny" pack. These free your hands but keep your camera within easy reach when needed.

✔ Charge your camera battery each night or have extra batteries available so your camera always has sufficient power.

✔ Carry extra memory cards. You don't want to miss out on a great shot because your memory card is full.

▲ Try to include people in your photos along with landmarks. Here children enjoy the spray from a geyser in Yellowstone National Park.

TIP #3: TAKE LOTS OF PICTURES

One advantage of digital cameras is that you can take lots and lots of photos, and then choose the ones you like best and want to keep. Digital memory cards can hold hundreds of photos compared to the 24 or 36 shots on a traditional roll of film. Photos can be viewed almost instantly on the camera's display screen, allowing you to view pictures you've taken and delete the ones you don't like. This frees up space on the memory card for even more pictures!

✔ Take as many pictures as you can. Try different angles, zoom in, zoom out - experiment!

✔ Balance the types of photos you take. Try to take just as

many pictures of people as you do things and places.

✔ Use the camera's display screen to review the photos you just took. If you are not happy with the results, take additional pictures.

✔ Each night, review the photos you took that day. Delete ones you don't like to free up additional space on the memory card.

TIP #4: GET IN THE PICTURE

The photographer is often absent from vacation photos because they are behind the camera taking all the pictures! Use these tips to make sure you get into some of the family vacation photos.

▲ Check your camera's display screen after you take a shot. If you aren't happy with the picture, take another one.

✔ Pass the camera to someone else. Share the photography duties with other family members, such as a brother or sister. Take turns so everyone has a chance to be in some of the photos.

✔ Use your camera's self-timer to get into the photo yourself. Steady your camera on a solid object such as a table or rock, or use a tripod. Hit the self-timer and run around to get in front of the lens. Most self-timers will give you 10 to 15 seconds to get ready before the picture is taken.

✔ Use more than one camera. If several members of your family carry a camera, everyone is sure to get into some of the photos.

TIP #5: TAKE CANDID SHOTS

Often vacation photographs look too posed with people standing in front of landmarks. Try capturing moments when people are not aware you are taking pictures. You'll get more relaxed, realistic photos that better depict your vacation experiences.

▲ Capture candid moments from your trip when people are unaware you are taking their picture.

✔ Don't pose too many pictures. Rather than asking people to stop, turn, and smile for the camera, take candid pictures of them enjoying the moment.

✔ Try taking some silly photos. Catch people being goofy, but don't have them pose for the camera.

✔ When shooting landmarks, choose your point of interest and compose your photo in the viewfinder. Then catch your family "being themselves" in the foreground.

✔ Look for quiet moments to capture - mom and dad studying a map, your brother reading in the hotel, or your sister enjoying an ice cream at the park.

✔ Remember to have fun taking your vacation pictures. Don't over-think your photos - just shoot!

▲ **Place your subject off-center to create a more natural balance in your photos.**

TIP #6: COMPOSE YOUR SHOTS

When you get ready to take a picture, take time to look through the viewfinder or LCD display. Take a close look to see what you are including and excluding in the photo. This is called composing the shot.

✔ Pick a point of interest, the visual focal point that is the main subject of your photo. This might be a person, such as a family member, or a thing, such as a statue or a mountain.

✔ Don't always place your subject in the center of the shot. Try shooting them off-center to the right or left for a more interesting perspective. This is sometimes called the "Rule of Thirds" because the best place to position the subject is along the outer third of the photo.

✔ Fill the rest of the frame with background which highlights where you are - a busy city street, a quiet mountain stream, or a colorful market.

▲ Zoom in close to fill the frame and capture people's facial expressions.

TIP #7: GET IN CLOSE

You'll get better photos if you zoom in close to your subjects. If you stand back too far, people and objects will look like tiny specks in the distance. Zooming in will allow you to capture details such as people's facial expressions. Fill the frame with only those things you want in the photo. Don't be afraid to use your feet to move closer to your subject or to get a shot from a different angle.

✔ Move in close or zoom in. Don't stand too far away. If possible, you should be within 6 feet of your subject.

✔ Back up to include more scenery. If you are including people in the picture, ask them to back up with you. Keeping them close will add depth to your photo.

✔ Include only as much of the background as is needed. Compose your shot. Is there something in the sky or the foreground you want to include?

✔ Take several photos of the same scene. Try different angles, perspectives, and settings.

Tip #8: Change Your Perspective

Many amateur photographers take all their pictures from the same straight-on perspective. Try changing the angle from which you take a picture. Lay on the ground and shoot looking up at your subject, or stand on a chair to get a higher perspective. Don't take all horizontal pictures. Turn your camera to compose vertical shots.

▲ Take pictures from a variety of angles to add interest to your photos.

✔ Experiment with different angles by looking through the viewfinder or LCD display before you take the picture.

✔ Move around. Crouch down, or stand on an object to get a picture looking down from above. Use your feet to look for creative shots!

✔ Don't back up to take pictures of tall subjects. Turn your camera to shoot vertically.

✔ Get down low and shoot vertically to compose very tall subjects (like a skyscraper).

✔ Try new things. Have fun while taking your photos!

Tip #9: Be Aware Of Backgrounds

▲ Turn your camera vertically to take pictures of tall subjects.

When you compose your photos, be sure to study the entire frame, not just the subject you are shooting. Make sure there is nothing distracting in the background like a lamp post or tree limb that appears to be sticking out of someone's head.

✔ Before you press the shutter button, take a moment to look at the background in the viewfinder. Does it complement your subject or is it distracting? Remember that all parts of the frame add up to make a photo.

✔ Zoom in or use your feet to move closer to your subject or use a different angle until the background is uncluttered.

✔ Use background to take interesting shots, such as a family member attempting to "hold up" a leaning building.

TIP #10: CHECK YOUR LIGHTING

Proper lighting can be the difference between a great shot and a poor one. Make sure you have enough light available, or use a flash. Many cameras have an automatic flash which goes on only when needed. But use your flash sparingly. Natural sunlight is best.

▲ Make sure there is nothing distracting in the photo's background, like an errant tree limb or lamp post.

✔ Keep the sun behind you or to the side. If the sun is behind your subject, it will cast a dark shadow over them.

✔ If you can't move so the sun is behind you, use your camera's flash to light your subject and minimize shadows.

✔ Keep taking pictures even if the sky turns gloomy or it starts to rain or snow. You can capture some dramatic shots during these less-than-ideal conditions.

✔ Try to avoid using a flash if possible. The flash on your camera will only light the area immediately in front of you, often resulting in poor pictures. Try shooting in low light without a flash. Use low lighting to be creative!

▲ **Shooting in low light without a flash can often yield dramatic results.**

TELLING A STORY WITH YOUR PHOTOS

Your pictures tell a story - the story of your vacation! Like all good stories, your vacation has a beginning, a middle, and an end. Make sure you cover all three in your photos. Rather than just taking a bunch of random pictures, think about how you want to "tell the story" of your vacation to your family and friends when you return home.

THE BEGINNING: START TAKING PHOTOS AT HOME

The beginning of your story includes all the planning and preparation as well as the travel to get to your destination.

Start taking pictures right away! Here are some ideas of things to shoot.

✔ Take pictures of family members packing bags for the trip.

✔ Capture your dad loading the car with luggage.

✔ Take a group photo of your family before you leave. Use your camera's self-timer or ask a friend to take the photo so you can be included.

▲ **Start taking pictures at the beginning of your trip - when you're packing the car, boarding the train, or waiting at the airport.**

✔ Get pictures of your family at the airport, boarding the train, taking the shuttle, or waiting for the bus to arrive.

✔ Shoot a close-up of your plane tickets or boarding passes.

✔ Photograph people who are part of your journey such as cab drivers, pilots, bus drivers, train conductors, and hotel staff. Catch them in action checking your bags, taking your tickets, etc.

THE MIDDLE: YOUR DESTINATION

Congratulations! You've reached your destination, as well as the middle of your story. This is the point where most people start taking pictures, but you're already deep into your photo journey. Keep documenting your travels with photos.

▲ Shots from behind can show emotion, such as this photo at the Flight 93 National Memorial in Pennsylvania.

✔ Take pictures of the places and landmarks you visit. Don't forget to include family members and others in some of your photos. Posed photos in front of landmarks are fine, but be sure to take some candid shots capturing people's expressions and their interactions at the location.

✔ Don't be afraid to shoot behind your subjects, capturing them looking up in awe at a snow-capped mountain or dancing to the rhythm of a street musician.

✔ Include photos along the way - in the car, on the road, at rest stops, etc.

✔ Take pictures of your hotel room, around the pool, and

at restaurants you visit.

✔ Use signs to introduce places. These serve as great chapter titles when creating a photo album or digital story. Take pictures of "Welcome to..." or "You are now entering..." signs. Photograph building marquees, historical plaques, street signs, and billboards. Have a family member hold a sign in front of a landmark.

▲ **Use signs to introduce new places and help tell your story.**

THE END: HEADING HOME

Like any good story, your photo journey needs an ending. Keep taking photos all the way to the end of your vacation. Record not only sites, but also people's actions and emotions as your trip comes to an end.

✔ Take photos of family members repacking and loading the car for the return trip home.

✔ Snap some final photos around your room. Capture your family leaving the hotel.

✔ Photograph the boat, plane, train, or bus you are traveling in.

▲ **Keep taking pictures at stops on the way home. Your vacation isn't finished yet!**

✔ Take pictures of your family at the boarding gate or collecting luggage at the baggage carousel.

✔ Capture people's emotions. Catch them napping or playing games to pass time.

✔ Take photos at rest stops and restaurants on the way home.

✔ Capture a few final shots after arriving back home. Take pictures of people unpacking the car, greeting friends and neighbors, or reuniting with family pets.

HAVE FUN WITH PHOTOGRAPHY

Above all, remember that these tips are suggestions, not rules you must follow. Don't worry if you cannot remember all these tips. You can always go back and review them occasionally to refresh your memory. Experiment and have fun with your photography!

WHAT'S NEXT?

Congratulations on completing your scavenger hunt around Chicago! You have uncovered clues, gathered points along the journey, and collected a well-deserved award. You have also kept a daily journal to record your travel memories and taken photos to document your adventure. Above all, you had a great time visiting Chicago!

When you return home, be sure to check out the digital storytelling page on the Scavenger Guides website. You will learn how to record your daily journal writings and combine them with digital pictures from your trip to create a multimedia travel video. This video is sure to become a treasured remembrance of your vacation for the entire family!

If you enjoyed this scavenger hunt around Chicago, check out our guides to other destinations. Visit http://www.scavengerguides.com to learn more.

Happy traveling!

▲ Gap of Dunloe, County Kerry, Ireland.

ABOUT THE AUTHOR

For as long as he can remember, Daniel Ireland has loved to travel. As a young boy, he traveled extensively throughout North America and Europe with his parents and three siblings. He now shares his passion for travel and adventure with his own family. When he's not on the road, he can be found in Grand Haven, Michigan, where he lives with his wife, Nancy, and their two children, Megan and Andrew.

19451751R00069

Made in the USA
Lexington, KY
19 December 2012